HEINEMANN MODULAR MATHEMATICS for
EDEXCEL AS AND A-LEVEL
Revise for Statistics 2

Greg Attwood Gill Dyer Gordon Skipworth

Success through qualifications

Heinemann Educational Publishers,
a division of Heinemann Publishers (Oxford) Ltd,
Halley Court, Jordan Hill, Oxford, OX2 8EJ

OXFORD   MELBOURNE   AUCKLAND   JOHANNESBURG
BLANTYRE   GABORONE   PORTSMOUTH NH (USA)   CHICAGO

First published 2001

05   04   03   02   01
10   9   8   7   6   5   4   3

ISBN 0 435 51117 3

Cover design by Gecko Limited

Original design by Geoffrey Wadsley; additional design work by Jim Turner

Typeset and illustrated by Tech-Set Limited, Gateshead, Tyne and Wear

Printed in Great Britain by Scotprint

Acknowledgements:

The publisher's and authors' thanks are due to Edexcel for permission to
reproduce questions from past examination papers. These are marked with an [E].

The answers have been provided by the authors and are not the responsibility of
the examining board.

About this book

This book is designed to help you get your best possible grade in your Statistics 2 examination. The authors are Chief and Principal examiners and moderators, and have a good understanding of Edexcel's requirements.

Revise for Statistics 2 covers the key topics that are tested in the Statistics 2 exam paper. You can use this book to help you revise at the end of your course, or you can use it throughout your course alongside the course textbook, *Heinemann Modular Mathematics for Edexcel AS and A-level Statistics 2*, which provides complete coverage of the syllabus.

Helping you prepare for your exam

To help you prepare, each topic offers you:

- **Key points to remember** – summarises the statistical ideas you need to know and be able to use.
- **Worked examples and examination questions** – help you understand and remember important methods, and show you how to set out your answers clearly.
- **Revision exercises** – help you practise using these important methods to solve problems. Exam-level questions are included so you can be sure you are reaching the right standard, and answers are given at the back of the book so you can assess your progress.
- **Test yourself questions** – help you see where you need extra revision and practice. If you do need extra help they show you where to look in the *Heinemann Modular Mathematics for Edexcel AS and A-level Statistics 2* textbook.

Exam practice and advice on revising

Examination style paper – this paper at the end of the book provides a set of questions of examination standard. It gives you an opportunity to practise taking a complete exam before you meet the real thing. The answers are given at the back of the book.

How to revise – for advice on revising before the exam, read the How to revise section on the next page.

How to revise using this book

Making the best use of your revision time

The topics in this book have been arranged in a logical sequence so you can work your way through them from beginning to end. But **how** you work on them depends on how much time there is between now and your examination.

If you have plenty of time before the exam then you can **work through each topic in turn**, covering the key points and worked examples before doing the revision exercises and test yourself questions.

If you are short of time then you can **work through the Test yourself sections** first, to help you see which topics you need to do further work on.

However much time you have to revise, make sure you break your revision into short blocks of about 40 minutes, separated by five- or ten-minute breaks. Nobody can study effectively for hours without a break.

Using the Test yourself sections

Each Test yourself section provides a set of key questions. Try each question:

- If you can do it and get the correct answer then move on to the next topic. Come back to this topic later to consolidate your knowledge and understanding by working through the key points, worked examples and revision exercises.

- If you cannot do the question, or get an incorrect answer or part answer, then work through the key points, worked examples and revision exercises before trying the Test yourself questions again. If you need more help, the cross-references beside each Test yourself question show you where to find relevant information in the *Heinemann Modular Mathematics for Edexcel AS and A-level Statistics 2* textbook.

Reviewing the key points

Most of the key points are straightforward ideas that you can learn: try to understand each one. Imagine explaining each idea to a friend in your own words, and say it out loud as you do so. This is a better way of making the ideas stick than just reading them silently from the page.

As you work through the book, remember to go back over key points from earlier topics at least once a week. This will help you to remember them in the exam.

The binomial distribution

Key points to remember

1 **Factorial notation**

$n! = n(n-1)(n-2)(n-3)\ldots(2)(1)$

Factorials may be calculated using the factorial button on your calculator.

2 **Arrangements** – If there are k different types of object with $n_1, n_2, \ldots, n_k$ of each type, the number of arrangements is

$$\frac{(n_1 + n_2 + \ldots + n_k)!}{n_1!\, n_2! \ldots n_k!}$$

3 **The Binomial theorem**

$$(x + y)^n = x^n + nx^{n-1}y + \frac{n(n-1)}{2!}x^{n-2}y^2 +$$

$$\ldots + \frac{n!}{r!(n-r)!}x^{n-r}y^r + \ldots + y^n$$

$\dfrac{n!}{r!(n-r)!}$ is often written as $\begin{pmatrix} n \\ r \end{pmatrix}$ or ^nC_r and is the number of combinations of r objects from n.

^nC_r may be calculated using the button available on most calculators.

4 **Conditions for a binomial distribution**

There must be a fixed number of trials (n).
The trials must be independent.
The outcome of a trial must be either success or failure.
The probability of success, p, must be constant.

5 **The binomial distribution** – If X is binomially distributed $X \sim \mathrm{B}(n, p)$, then

$$\mathrm{P}(X = r) = \begin{pmatrix} n \\ r \end{pmatrix} p^r(1-p)^{n-r} \qquad r = 0, 1, 2, \ldots, n$$

X represents the number of successes in n trials, p the probability of success. The distribution is written as $\mathrm{B}(n, p)$.

When finding $\mathrm{P}(X \geqslant r)$ etc, consider using $1 - \mathrm{P}(X < r)$ if that involves calculating fewer terms.

> **6** **The mean of a binomial distribution** – If $X \sim B(n, p)$ then $\mu = E(X) = np$.
>
> **7** **The variance of a binomial distribution** – If $X \sim B(n, p)$ then $\sigma^2 = \text{Var}(X) = np(1 - p)$ or npq where $q = (1 - p)$.
>
> **8** **Cumulative probability statistics tables for binomial distributions** – Table 1 on page 121 of Book S2 gives cumulative probabilities for $n = 5$, 10 and 20, and for $p = 0.05$ to 0.5 in steps of 0.05. The Edexcel booklet of Mathematical Formulae and Statistical Tables gives cumulative probabilities for many other values of n.

It is quicker to use **6** and **7** to calculate the mean and variance rather than using $\sum x P(X = x)$ and $\sum x^2 P(X = x) - \mu^2$.

Always use the tables if possible.

The formulae in **5** **6** and **7** are given in the formulae booklet.

Example 1

Find the term of the expansion of $(p + q)^8$ that contains p^5.

Answer

Using **3**, the term containing p^5 will be of the form kp^5q^3.

The coefficient k will be $= \begin{pmatrix} 8 \\ 5 \end{pmatrix}$

$$= \frac{8!}{5!3!} = \frac{8 \times 7 \times 6 \times 5 \times 4 \times 3 \times 2 \times 1}{5 \times 4 \times 3 \times 2 \times 1 \times 3 \times 2 \times 1} = \frac{8 \times 7 \times 6}{3 \times 2 \times 1}$$
$$= 56$$

The term will be $56p^5q^3$.

Example 2

(a) State the conditions under which a binomial distribution may be used as a model.

(b) Which of the following can be modelled by a binomial distribution? If they cannot, give reasons.

    (i)   The number of left-handed pupils in a class of 16.

    (ii) The number of red balls drawn in a sample of 6 from a bag containing 8 red balls and 10 green balls.

    (iii) The number of tosses of a fair coin before a head appears.

    (iv) The number of heads when a biased coin is tossed 5 times.

Answer

(a) There must be a fixed number of trials. The trials must be independent. The trials must have only two outcomes: success or failure. The probability of success must be constant.

Using **4**

(b) (i) and (iv) can be modelled by a binomial distribution. (Note that although the coin is biased in (iv) the probability of getting a head is constant.)

(ii) Cannot be modelled by a binomial distribution because if you take a sample of 6 from the bag the probability of getting a red is not constant. (You would have to draw the balls separately and replace each ball after it was drawn for a binomial model.)

(iii) Cannot be modelled by a binomial distribution because the number of times the coin is tossed (n) is not fixed.

Example 3

In a mathematics examination with a large entry, 80% of the candidates are known to have passed. After marking, the chief examiner decides to take a random sample of 12 scripts.

Find the probability that:

(a) exactly 5 of the scripts are those of failed candidates

(b) fewer than 4 of the scripts are those of failed candidates.

Answer

Although the sample is taken without replacement, the number of scripts is large, and the probability of selecting a script that is a failure will vary by such a small amount that a binomial distribution will still give a good approximation. If X represents the number of failed scripts then X is modelled by B(12, 0.2).

(a) $P(X = 5) = \dfrac{12!}{5!7!}p^5(1 - p)^7$

$= 792(0.2)^5(0.8)^7$

$= 792 \times 0.000\,32 \times 0.2097$

$= 0.0532 = 0.0532$ (3 s.f.)

Using **5**

Note we are looking for failed scripts so p is the probability of a failed script.

(b) $P(X < 4) = P(X = 3) + P(X = 2) + P(X = 1) + P(X = 0)$

$= {}^{12}C_3(0.2)^3(0.8)^9 + {}^{12}C_2(0.2)^2(0.8)^{10} + {}^{12}C_1(0.2)^1(0.8)^{11} + (0.8)^{12}$

Using **5**

$= 220 \times 0.008 \times 0.1342 + 66 \times 0.04 \times 0.1074 + 12 \times 0.2 \times 0.0859 + 0.0687$

$= 0.7946 = 0.795$ (3 s.f.)

Example 4

A multiple-choice examination consists of 10 questions, each with four possible answers. A candidate, not knowing any of the answers, decides to select one answer to each question at random.

(a) Write down the probability distribution for the number of correct answers, and work out the various probabilities.

(b) Given that the pass mark is 6 correct questions out of 10, calculate the candidate's chance of passing the examination.

(c) Find the pass mark for a candidate to have a 50% or greater chance of passing.

Answer

(a) The probability of a correct answer is 0.25, and there are 10 trials. Let X represent the number of correct answers selected by the candidate. Then $X \sim$ B(10, 0.25).

Using **4**

The probability function is

$$P(X = r) = \binom{10}{r} 0.25^r (1 - 0.25)^{10 - r} \qquad r = 0, 1, 2, \ldots, 10 \qquad \boxed{\text{Using } \boxed{5}}$$

Using $\boxed{8}$,

$P(X = 0) = 0.0563$
$P(X = 1) = 0.2440 - 0.0563 = 0.1877$
$P(X = 2) = 0.5256 - 0.2440 = 0.2816$
$P(X = 3) = 0.7759 - 0.5256 = 0.2503$
$P(X = 4) = 0.9219 - 0.7759 = 0.1460$
$P(X = 5) = 0.9803 - 0.9219 = 0.0584$
$P(X = 6) = 0.9965 - 0.9803 = 0.0162$
$P(X = 7) = 0.9996 - 0.9965 = 0.0031$
$P(X = 8) = 1.0000 - 0.9996 = 0.0004$
$P(X = 9) = 1.0000 - 1.0000 = 0.0000$
$P(X = 10) = 1.0000 - 1.0000 = 0.0000$

> The cumulative values for this distribution may be obtained from the table. e.g.
> $P(X = 3) = P(X \leqslant 3) - P(X \leqslant 2)$

(b) The probability of five or fewer correct answers is 0.9803 so the probability of 6 or more correct is $1 - 0.9803 = 0.0197$.

(c) For the probability of a pass to be 0.5 or greater the probability of a fail must be < 0.5.
From the table

$\quad$ P(2 or fewer correct) $= 0.5256$
$\quad$ P(1 or fewer correct) $= 0.2440$

The pass mark would have to be set at 1.

Example 5

Rainfall records collected over many years in a certain holiday resort show that it rains on average 2 days in every 5.

(a) Calculate the probability that in any randomly chosen week:
$\quad$ (i) $\quad$ rain will fall on exactly three of the days
$\quad$ (ii) $\quad$ there will be more wet days than dry days.

(b) A family decides to take a 3-week holiday in the area. Allowing a day for travelling this means they will spend 20 days there. If W is the number of wet days on their holiday calculate:
$\quad$ (i) $\quad$ E(W) and Var(W)
$\quad$ (ii) $\quad$ the probability of them having fewer than 10 wet days.

Answer

(a) $W \sim B\left(7, \frac{2}{5}\right)$

$$P(W = 3) = \binom{7}{3} \left(\tfrac{2}{5}\right)^3 \left(\tfrac{3}{5}\right)^4 = \frac{7!}{3!4!} \times \left(\tfrac{2}{5}\right)^3 \times \left(\tfrac{3}{5}\right)^4$$

$$= 35 \times 0.064 \times 0.1296$$
$$= 0.2903$$
$$= 0.290 \text{ (3 d.p.)}$$

(ii) More wet days than fine days means 4, 5, 6, or 7 wet days.

$P(W > 3) = P(W = 4) + P(W = 5) + P(W = 6) + P(W = 7)$

$$= \binom{7}{4} \left(\tfrac{2}{5}\right)^4 \left(\tfrac{3}{5}\right)^3 + \binom{7}{5} \left(\tfrac{2}{5}\right)^5 \left(\tfrac{3}{5}\right)^2 + \binom{7}{6} \left(\tfrac{2}{5}\right)^6 \left(\tfrac{3}{5}\right)^1 + \binom{7}{7} \left(\tfrac{2}{5}\right)^7 \left(\tfrac{3}{5}\right)^0$$

$$= 0.1935 + 0.0774 + 0.0172 + 0.0016$$

$$= 0.2898 = 0.290 \text{ (3 d.p.)}$$

(b) $W \sim B(20, 0.4)$

  (i) $E(W) = np$

  $= 20 \times 0.4$

  $= 8$

  $\text{Var}(W) = np(1 - p)$

  $= 20 \times 0.4 \times 0.6$

  $= 4.8$

  (ii) $P(W < 10) = P(W \leqslant 9)$

From the table (Binomial cumulative distribution function)

  $P(W < 10) = 0.7553$

Example 6

If $X \sim B(15, 0.4)$ calculate:

(a) $E(3X + 2)$

(b) $\text{Var}(4X + 3)$

Answer

(a) $E(X) = np$

  $= 15 \times 0.4$

  $= 6$

$E(3X + 2) = 3E(X) + 2$

  $= 3 \times 6 + 2$

  $= 20$

(b) $\text{Var}(X) = np(1 - p)$

  $= 15 \times 0.4 \times 0.6$

  $= 3.6$

$\text{Var}(4X + 3) = 4^2 \text{Var}(X)$

  $= 16 \times 3.6$

  $= 57.6$

> Here you use the formulae for the expectation and variance of a linear function of a random variable, $E(aX + b) = aE(X) + b$ and $\text{Var}(aX + b) = a^2\text{Var}(X)$ (see Book S1 page 159).

Worked examination question 1 [E]

State two assumptions associated with the use of the binomial distribution.

The probability that a component intended for use in a computer passes a purity test is 0.038.

(a) In a batch of 10 randomly selected components find the probability that:

  (i)   none of the components pass the test,

  (ii) fewer than three components pass the test.

(b) Let n be the smallest number of components which need to be examined before there is at least a 90% chance that one or more of them will have passed the test.

  (i)   Show that n satisfies $(0.962)^n \leqslant 0.10$.

  (ii) Given that $(0.962)^{58} = 0.1057$, find the value of n.

Answer

Two assumptions: there are a fixed number of trials; each trial results in success or failure. Alternative assumptions are: independent trials; constant probability of success. Any two from the four in 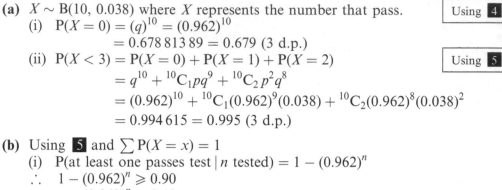 4 are acceptable for this answer.

(a) $X \sim B(10, 0.038)$ where X represents the number that pass.   Using **4**

   (i) $P(X = 0) = (q)^{10} = (0.962)^{10}$
   $= 0.678\,813\,89 = 0.679$ (3 d.p.)

   (ii) $P(X < 3) = P(X = 0) + P(X = 1) + P(X = 2)$ Using **5**
   $= q^{10} + {}^{10}C_1 pq^9 + {}^{10}C_2 p^2 q^8$
   $= (0.962)^{10} + {}^{10}C_1(0.962)^9(0.038) + {}^{10}C_2(0.962)^8(0.038)^2$
   $= 0.994\,615 = 0.995$ (3 d.p.)

(b) Using **5** and $\sum P(X = x) = 1$

   (i) $P(\text{at least one passes test} \mid n \text{ tested}) = 1 - (0.962)^n$
   $\therefore \quad 1 - (0.962)^n \geqslant 0.90$
   $\therefore \qquad\quad (0.962)^n \leqslant 0.10$

   (ii) $(0.962)^{58} = 0.1057$
   $(0.962)^{59} = 0.1017$
   $(0.962)^{60} = 0.0978$
   $\therefore \quad n = 60$

Revision exercise 1A

1   Given that there are equal numbers of boys and girls born, find the probability that a family of six children which has been chosen at random has:

   (a) more girls than boys,   **(b)** five boys in it.

2   A large number of printed circuit boards (p.c.b.s) for use in measuring equipment have their various electrical components soldered into position by two people, Jayesh and Sally. The probability that a p.c.b. produced by Jayesh has a fault when tested is 0.05, while the probability that a p.c.b. produced by Sally has a fault is 0.15.

   (a) Find the probability that in a random sample of 4 p.c.b.s produced by Jayesh, one is faulty.

   (b) Using tables or otherwise, show that in a random sample of 20 p.c.b.s produced by Sally the probability that not more than three will be faulty is > 0.5.

3 In an examination with a very large entry the probability that a candidate passes is 0.70. The chief examiner selects at random 20 marked scripts.

(a) Write down the appropriate distribution to model the number of scripts, in a random sample of 20, that belong to candidates who have failed.

(b) Find the probability that:

    (i) exactly 5 of the scripts are those of failed candidates,

    (ii) there are more than 8 scripts belonging to failed candidates.

4 A policeman is carrying out roadside checks on cars to see if they have any defective tyres. The probability that a car has defective tyres is 0.08.

(a) If he stops 20 cars, suggest a suitable model for the distribution of X, the number of cars with defective tyres.

(b) Copy and complete the following table.

x	0	1	2	3	4	5	6 or more
P($X = x$)	0.1887			0.1414	0.0523	0.0145	

Find the probability that the policeman will find:

(c) fewer than 4 cars with defective tyres,

(d) more than 3 cars with defective tyres.

5 The random variable X has probability distribution B(20, 0.25).

The random variable Y has probability distribution B(10, 0.4).

(a) Find E($3X + 4$).

(b) Find Var($3 + 4Y$).

Test yourself	What to review
	If your answer is incorrect:
1 Evaluate $\dfrac{8!}{5!2!}$	*Review Heinemann Book S2 pages 7–10*

2 Items in a workshop are to be colour coded using thin strips of coloured paper.
Each item will have a different code consisting of 7 strips of blue paper and 4 strips of red paper.
(a) How many arrangements can be made of these strips of paper?

It is decided that there are not enough arrangements to cover the number of items to be coded so an additional piece of red paper is added.
(b) How many items can now be coded?

Review Heinemann Book S2 pages 7–10

---

3 Calculate the term in the expansion of $(a + b)^6$ that contains a^3.

Review Heinemann Book S2 pages 10–12

---

4 A youth club runs two five-a-side soccer teams and has ten regular members. The club calls upon a reserve if a regular member is unable to play. The probability of any regular member being absent is 0.15. Using the binomial table on page 121 of Book S2, calculate the probability that on a particular randomly chosen occasion:
(a) exactly one regular member is unavailable,
(b) more than two regular members are unavailable.

Review Heinemann Book S2 pages 13–19

---

5 Certain currency notes were made with one metal strip running through them. Later it was decided to add a second metal strip to increase security. For some time both types of note were in circulation, and the probability of a note having two strips was 0.3.
Calculate the probability that in a random sample of 8 notes:
(a) exactly three would have two metal strips,
(b) fewer than three would have two metal strips,
(c) more than three would have one metal strip.

Review Heinemann Book S2 pages 13–19

---

6 A fair octagonal die is thrown 20 times, and the random variable X represents the number of eights thrown.
Find the mean and variance of X.

Review Heinemann Book S2 pages 20–22

Test yourself answers

1 168 **2 (a)** 330 **(b)** 792 **3** $20a^3b^3$ **4 (a)** 0.3474 **(b)** 0.1798 **5 (a)** 0.2541 **(b)** 0.5518 **(c)** 0.9420
6 Mean $= 2\frac{1}{2}$, Variance $= 2\frac{3}{16}$

Key points to remember

1 **Exponential function**

$$e^\lambda = \lambda^0 + \frac{\lambda^1}{1!} + \frac{\lambda^2}{2!} + \frac{\lambda^3}{3!} + \dots$$

2 **Conditions for a Poisson distribution**

Events must occur:
- **independently** of each other,
- **singly** in space or time,
- at a **constant rate** in that the mean number in an interval is proportional to the length of the interval. (Sometimes called random events.)

3 **The Poisson distribution** – If X has a Poisson distribution $X \sim \text{Po}(\lambda)$, then

$$P(X = r) = \frac{e^{-\lambda}\lambda^r}{r!}, \qquad \text{for } r = 0, 1, 2, 3, \dots$$

The Poisson distribution has a single parameter λ, and is written $\text{Po}(\lambda)$.

There are an infinite number of values for r and so an infinite number of probabilities. It is usual to put together all the small terms at the end as $P(X \geqslant n)$ for some n, the value of n depending on the problem.

$P(X \geqslant n)$ can be found by using **4** and subtracting the sum of the other values from 1.

It is easier to calculate each successive term by using the fact that the rth term is $\frac{\lambda}{r}$ times the $(r-1)$th term $\left(\text{e.g. the 4th term} = \text{3rd term} \times \frac{\lambda}{4}\right)$.

4 **Sum of probabilities**

$$\sum P(X = r) = 1$$

5 **The mean of a Poisson distribution** – If $X \sim \text{Po}(\lambda)$ then

$$\mu = E(X) = \lambda$$

6 **The variance of a Poisson distribution** – If $X \sim \text{Po}(\lambda)$ then

$$\sigma^2 = \text{Var}(X) = \lambda$$

The formulae in **3**, **5** and **6** are given in the formulae booklet.

7 **Probability tables for Poisson distribution** – Table 2, giving cumulative probabilities for $\lambda = 0.5$ to 10 in steps of 0.5, is given on page 122 of Book S2.

Use the Poisson cumulative probability table whenever you can.

> **8** **The Poisson distribution as an approximation to the binomial distribution** – If $X \sim B(n, p)$ and if n is large and p small then $X \approx Po(np)$.

Watch out for questions on binomial distributions that have large values for n and small probabilities; these are usually answered using a Poisson approximation. (See Example 2.)

Example 1
Given that $X \sim Po(3)$, calculate:
(a) $P(X = 6)$
(b) $P(X = 7)$
(c) $P(X > 2)$
(d) $P(2 < X < 6)$

Answer

(a) Using **3**,
$$P(X = 6) = \frac{e^{-\lambda}\lambda^6}{6!} = \frac{e^{-3}3^6}{720} = 0.0504$$

The rth term is $\dfrac{\lambda}{r}$ times the $(r - 1)$th term. See tip next to key point **3**. Always use the quickest method.

(b) $P(X = 7) = P(X = 6) \times \dfrac{\lambda}{7} = 0.0504 \times \dfrac{3}{7} = 0.0216$

(c) $P(X > 2) = 1 - P(X \leqslant 2)$
$= 1 - 0.4232$
$= 0.5768$

Using **4**

Using **7** (table of cumulative values)

(d) $P(2 < X < 6) = P(X \leqslant 5) - P(X \leqslant 2) = 0.9161 - 0.4232 = 0.4929$

Example 2
A botanist is working in a field studying the distribution of plantains. The field is divided into 200 small quadrants each having an area of $1\,m^2$.
If the distribution of the plantains is assumed to be Poisson with a mean of 2, calculate:
(a) the probability that a quadrant chosen at random contains exactly 8 plantains,
(b) the probability that the botanist finds no quadrants containing exactly 8 plantains.

Answer

(a) Let X represent the number of plantains in a quadrant.
The mean of a Poisson $= \lambda$, so $X \sim Po(2)$.
$$P(X = 8) = \frac{e^{-\lambda}\lambda^8}{8!} = \frac{e^{-2}2^8}{40\,320} = 0.000\,8593 = 0.000\,859 \ (3 \text{ s.f.})$$

Using **5**

(b) Let Y represent the number of quadrants (within the 200) that contain 8 plantains.
$Y \sim B(200, 0.000\,8593) \approx Po(200 \times 0.000\,8593) = Po(0.1719)$
So $P(Y = 0) = e^{-0.1719} = 0.842$

Note that $n = 200$ is large and $p = 0.000\,859$ is small. Hence the Poisson approximation to the binomial distribution can be used.

Example 3

A government minister believes that a crisis hits her department at the rate of 12 crises a year. She has just had 4 crises within a fortnight and wishes to have a model so that she can predict the probability of such a combination of events happening again. A civil servant suggests that a Poisson model would be appropriate.
(a) State the assumptions that must be made in order for a Poisson model to be used in this case.

If a Poisson model is assumed calculate:
(b) the probability that 4 crises occur in a given fortnight,
(c) the probability that there will be at most 1 week in any year with exactly 2 crises in it.

Answer

(a) The assumptions are: crises are independent of each other; they occur singly; their occurrence is random.

Using **2**

(b) The average number of crises occurring in any fortnight is $\frac{2}{52} \times 12 = 0.4615$.
Let X be the number of crises in any given fortnight.
$$X \sim \text{Po}(0.4615)$$
$$P(X = 4) = e^{-0.4615}\frac{0.4615^4}{4!}$$

Using **3**

$$= 0.001\,19$$

(c) The average number of crises per week $= \frac{1}{52} \times 12 = 0.230\,77$.
Let Y be the number of crises in any given week.
Then $Y \sim \text{Po}(0.230\,77)$
$$P(Y = 2) = e^{-0.230\,77}\frac{0.230\,77^2}{2!}$$
$$= 0.021\,14$$
Let Z be the number of weeks in a year with 2 crises.
$$Z \sim \text{B}(52, 0.021\,14)$$
So $Z \approx \text{Po}(52 \times 0.021\,14) = \text{Po}(1.0993)$

Using

$$P(Z < 2) = P(Z = 0) + P(Z = 1)$$

Using **3**

$$= e^{-1.0993} + e^{-1.0993}(1.0993)$$
$$= 0.3331 + 0.3662$$
$$= 0.699$$

Worked examination question 1 [E]

A television repair company uses a particular spare part at a rate of 4 per week. Assuming that requests for this spare part occur at random, find the probability that:
(a) exactly 6 are used in a particular week,
(b) at least 10 are used in a two-week period,
(c) exactly 6 are used in each of 3 consecutive weeks.

The manager decides to replenish the stock of this spare part to a constant level n at the start of each week.
(d) Find the smallest value of n such that, on average, the stock will be insufficient no more than once in a 52-week year.

Answer

Let $W = $ number of parts used in a week.
$$W \sim \text{Po}(4)$$

(a) $P(W = 6) = \dfrac{e^{-4} \times 4^6}{6!}$, using **3**, or $P(W = 6) = P(W \leqslant 6) - P(\text{W} \leqslant 5)$, using **7**,

$$= \dfrac{e^{-4} \times 4096}{720} = 0.1042 \quad \textbf{or} \quad = 0.8893 - 0.7851 = 0.1042$$

(b) Let $F = $ number of spare parts in a two-week period.
So $F \sim \text{Po}(8)$
Using **4**, $P(F \geqslant 10) = 1 - P(F \leqslant 9)$
$$= 1 - 0.7166 = 0.2834$$

Using **7**

(c) $P(W = 6$ in 3 consecutive weeks)
$= P(W = 6$ on a particular week$)^3$

Using the fact that these are independent events.

$$= 0.1042^3$$
$$= 0.001\,13$$

Using the answer to part (a)

(d) You require that $P(W > n) \leqslant \frac{1}{52}$
$$\Rightarrow P(W \leqslant n) \geqslant 1 - \frac{1}{52} = 0.981$$
From tables $P(W \leqslant 8) = 0.9786$ and $P(W \leqslant 9) = 0.9919$
$\therefore$ You need $n = 9$.

Using **7**

Revision exercise 1B

1 On a biology field trip students are required to study life in a small stream. One study involves looking at the number of micro-organisms in the stream. From previous studies it is known that 1 litre of water contains 600 micro-organisms.
If a student collects a $1\,\text{cm}^3$ sample at random, calculate the probability that the sample contains:
(a) no micro-organisms,
(b) more than 2 micro-organisms.

2 Seismic earth tremors occur independently and singly. One area on the edge of one of the Earth's tectonic plates has been found to have an average of 48 tremors per year. Calculate the probability that in any given month:
(a) exactly six tremors occur,
(b) fewer than 2 tremors occur,
(c) more than 2 tremors occur.

3 The probability that a match will not strike is 0.009.
Calculate the probability that in a box of 100 matches:
(a) they all strike satisfactorily,
(b) at least 2 do not strike.

4 A company produces large quantities of a particular electrical
component and knows from past experience that 20% of its
production will be classified as 'faulty'.
A random sample of 20 components is taken from the
production line.
(a) Write down an approximate distribution to model the
number of 'faulty' components in a sample of size 20.
(b) Find the probability that:
    (i)   there are exactly 2 'faulty' components in the sample,
    (ii) there are more than 4 'faulty' components in the
    sample.
(c) Using a Poisson approximation find the probability that
the number of 'faulty' components in this sample is between
5 and 8 (inclusive).

5 From previous experience of word-processing her work, a
sociology student is known to make an average of 1.5 errors
per complete page. The numbers of errors on different pages
are independent.
(a) Suggest a suitable model to describe the number of errors
per complete page made by this student.
(b) Find the probability that on a randomly chosen page
there are more than 4 errors.

The student word processes an essay that has 4 complete
pages.
(c) Find the probability that the essay will contain exactly
10 errors.   [E]

Test yourself	What to review

1 If $X \sim \text{Po}(2)$ calculate
   (a) $\text{P}(X = 1)$
   (b) $\text{P}(X \leqslant 3)$
   (c) $\text{P}(X > 2)$
   (d) $\text{P}(1 \leqslant X \leqslant 5)$

Review Heinemann Book S2 pages 22–29

2 **(a)** Write down three conditions that should apply when using a Poisson distribution.
   (b) Give an important property of a Poisson distribution.

Review Heinemann Book S2 pages 22–24

3 In a small village school there are an average of six absences per fortnight. It is decided that, to encourage better attendance, an extra long playtime will be given on the Friday afternoon of any week in which there are no absences. Assuming that the incentive has no effect, calculate the probability that:
   (a) in any given week there will be no absences,
   (b) in a term of 14 weeks the pupils will get an extra long playtime in more than 4 of the weeks.

Review Heinemann Book S2 pages 22–29

4 **(a)** What are the conditions under which a Poisson distribution can approximate a binomial distribution?
   (b) An engineering firm makes widgets. It has found that 3% of widgets have a fault in them. If a sample of 100 widgets is taken, find using a Poisson approximation, the probability that there will be fewer than 3 faulty widgets in the sample.

Review Heinemann Book S2 pages 29–32

Test yourself answers

1 **(a)** 0.2707 **(b)** 0.8571 **(c)** 0.3233 **(d)** 0.8481
2 **(a)** Events are: (i) independent of each other (ii) occur singly in space or time, and (iii) occur at a constant rate.
   (b) Infinite number of values of r, mean = variance, other suitable answer.
3 **(a)** 0.0498 **(b)** 0.0004   4 n large and p small **(b)** 0.4232

Continuous random variables

2

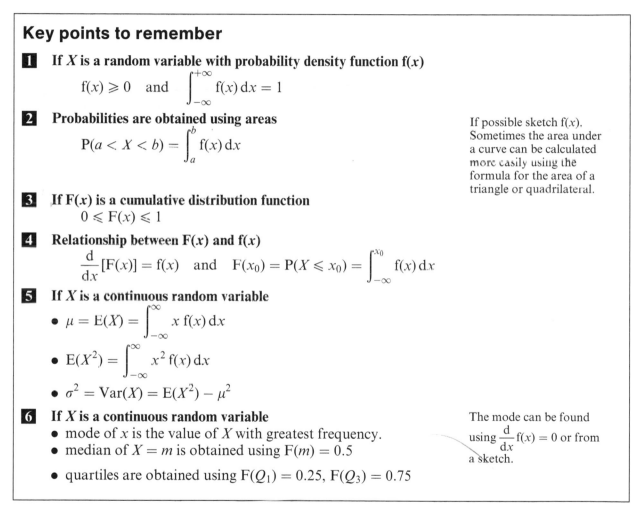

Key points to remember

1 **If X is a random variable with probability density function $f(x)$**

$$f(x) \geqslant 0 \quad \text{and} \quad \int_{-\infty}^{+\infty} f(x)\,dx = 1$$

2 **Probabilities are obtained using areas**

$$P(a < X < b) = \int_{a}^{b} f(x)\,dx$$

If possible sketch $f(x)$. Sometimes the area under a curve can be calculated more easily using the formula for the area of a triangle or quadrilateral.

3 **If $F(x)$ is a cumulative distribution function**
$$0 \leqslant F(x) \leqslant 1$$

4 **Relationship between $F(x)$ and $f(x)$**
$$\frac{d}{dx}[F(x)] = f(x) \quad \text{and} \quad F(x_0) = P(X \leqslant x_0) = \int_{-\infty}^{x_0} f(x)\,dx$$

5 **If X is a continuous random variable**
- $\mu = E(X) = \int_{-\infty}^{\infty} x\,f(x)\,dx$

- $E(X^2) = \int_{-\infty}^{\infty} x^2\,f(x)\,dx$

- $\sigma^2 = \text{Var}(X) = E(X^2) - \mu^2$

6 **If X is a continuous random variable**
- mode of x is the value of X with greatest frequency.
- median of $X = m$ is obtained using $F(m) = 0.5$
- quartiles are obtained using $F(Q_1) = 0.25$, $F(Q_3) = 0.75$

The mode can be found using $\dfrac{d}{dx} f(x) = 0$ or from a sketch.

Example 1
State which of the following can be described as discrete and which as continuous random variables.
(a) The amount of chocolate, in grams, consumed by a randomly selected student revising for the S2 examination.
(b) The mark, out of 75, scored by a randomly selected student in the S2 examination.
(c) The amount of sleep, in hours, that a randomly selected student has the night before taking the S2 examination.

Answer

(a) Can take any value in a range, so continuous.
(b) Only whole numbers are possible, so discrete.
(c) Can take any value in a range, so continuous.

Example 2

The continuous random variable X has probability density function

$$f(x) \begin{cases} 2 - \frac{2}{3}x, & 1 \leqslant x \leqslant 2 \\ 0, & \text{otherwise} \end{cases}$$

(a) Sketch the probability density function.
(b) Find $E(X)$.
(c) Show that $\text{Var}(X) = \frac{13}{162}$

Answer

(a)

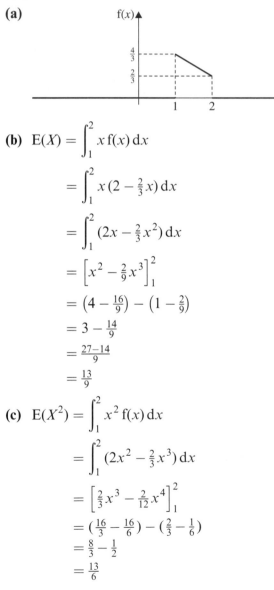

> Label the axes and mark appropriate values on them. Indicate $f(x)$ clearly for $x > 2$ and $x < 1$.

(b) $E(X) = \displaystyle\int_1^2 x\,f(x)\,dx$

Using ▣5

$$= \int_1^2 x\left(2 - \tfrac{2}{3}x\right) dx$$

$$= \int_1^2 \left(2x - \tfrac{2}{3}x^2\right) dx$$

$$= \left[x^2 - \tfrac{2}{9}x^3\right]_1^2$$

$$= \left(4 - \tfrac{16}{9}\right) - \left(1 - \tfrac{2}{9}\right)$$

$$= 3 - \tfrac{14}{9}$$

$$= \tfrac{27-14}{9}$$

$$= \tfrac{13}{9}$$

(c) $E(X^2) = \displaystyle\int_1^2 x^2\,f(x)\,dx$

Using ▣5

$$= \int_1^2 \left(2x^2 - \tfrac{2}{3}x^3\right) dx$$

$$= \left[\tfrac{2}{3}x^3 - \tfrac{2}{12}x^4\right]_1^2$$

$$= \left(\tfrac{16}{3} - \tfrac{16}{6}\right) - \left(\tfrac{2}{3} - \tfrac{1}{6}\right)$$

$$= \tfrac{8}{3} - \tfrac{1}{2}$$

$$= \tfrac{13}{6}$$

$$\text{Var}(X) = \sigma^2 = \text{E}(X^2) - \mu^2$$
$$\therefore \quad \sigma^2 = \tfrac{13}{6} - \left(\tfrac{13}{9}\right)^2$$
$$= \tfrac{351-338}{162}$$
$$= \tfrac{13}{162}$$

Using **5**

Example 3

The sketch below shows the probability density function f(x) of the continuous random variable X where

$$f(x) = \begin{cases} -kx(x+2), & -2 \leqslant x \leqslant 0, \\ 0, & \text{otherwise.} \end{cases}$$

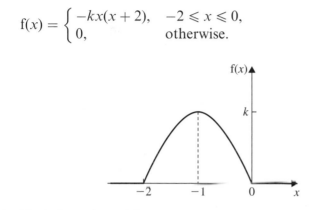

(a) Find the value of k.
(b) Write down E(X).
(c) Find P($X > -0.5$).

Answer

(a) $\displaystyle\int_{-\infty}^{\infty} f(x)\,dx = 1$

Using **1**

So $\displaystyle -k\int_{-2}^{0} (x^2 + 2x)\,dx = 1$

$$-k\left[\frac{x^3}{3} + x^2\right]_{-2}^{0} = 1$$

$$-k[(0) - (-\tfrac{8}{3} + 4)] = 1$$

i.e. $\qquad \tfrac{4}{3}k = 1$

so $\qquad k = \tfrac{3}{4}$

(b) E(X) = -1

By symmetry

(c) P($X > -0.5$) = $\displaystyle -\tfrac{3}{4}\int_{-0.5}^{0} (x^2 + 2x)\,dx$

$$= -\tfrac{3}{4}\left[\frac{x^3}{3} + x^2\right]_{-0.5}^{0}$$

$$= -\tfrac{3}{4}[(0) - (-\tfrac{1}{24} + \tfrac{1}{4})]$$

$$= \tfrac{3}{4} \times \tfrac{5}{24} = \tfrac{5}{32}$$

Example 4

The random variable X has probability density function f(x) given by

$$f(x) = \begin{cases} \frac{3}{2}(1 - x^2), & 0 \leqslant x \leqslant 1, \\ 0, & \text{otherwise.} \end{cases}$$

(a) Find the cumulative distribution function for all x.
(b) Find $P(X \leqslant 0.30)$ and $P(X > 0.35)$.
(c) Explain why the median of X lies between 0.30 and 0.35.

Answer

(a) $F(x_0) = \frac{3}{2} \displaystyle\int_0^{x_0} (1 - x^2)\, dx$ Using 4

$\qquad = \frac{3}{2} \left[x - \frac{1}{3}x^3 \right]_0^{x_0}$

$\qquad = \frac{3}{2}(x_0 - \frac{1}{3}x_0^3) - (0)$

So $F(x) = \begin{cases} 0, & x \leqslant 0, \\ \frac{3}{2}(x - \frac{1}{3}x^3), & 0 < x \leqslant 1, \\ 1, & x > 1. \end{cases}$ Remember to state F(x) for all values of x.

(b) $P(X \leqslant 0.30) = F(0.30)$

$\qquad\qquad = 1.5 \times (0.3 - \frac{1}{3} \times 0.3^3)$

$\qquad\qquad = 0.4365$

$\quad P(X > 0.35) = 1 - F(0.35)$

$\qquad\qquad = 1 - 1.5 \times (0.35 - \frac{1}{3} \times 0.35^3)$

$\qquad\qquad = 1 - 0.5035 = 0.4964$

(c) We know that $F(m) = 0.5$.   Using 6
From part **(b)** $F(0.30) < 0.5$ and $F(0.35) > 0.5$, so the median m must lie between 0.30 and 0.35.

Worked examination question 1[E]

A gardener is attempting to light a bonfire. The times, in minutes, for which a taper will stay alight on a calm day is modelled by the random variable T. The cumulative distribution function of T is given by

$$F(t) = P(T \leqslant t) = \begin{cases} 0, & t < 0, \\ \frac{1}{2}t^3 - \frac{3}{16}t^4, & 0 \leqslant t \leqslant 2, \\ 1, & t > 2. \end{cases}$$

(a) Find $P(T \leqslant 1)$.
(b) Verify that the median m of T satisfies $1.22 < m < 1.23$
(c) Find the probability density function f(t) of T.
(d) Find the modal time for which a taper will stay alight.
(e) Sketch the probability density function of T.
(f) Give a reason why this model may not be suitable on a windy day and give a sketch of a probability density function that may be more suitable in such conditions.

Answer

(a) $P(T \leq 1) = \frac{1}{2}(1^3) - \frac{3}{16}(1^4)$

$\qquad\qquad = \frac{5}{16}$ or 0.3125.

(b) The median is the value that splits the distribution into two equal parts.

Thus $P(T \leq m) = P(T \geq m) = \frac{1}{2}$.

Or, using **6**, $F(m) = 0.5$

In this situation $P(T \leq 1.22) = \frac{1}{2}(1.22)^3 - \frac{3}{16}(1.22)^4 = 0.492\,55$

and $\qquad\qquad P(T \leq 1.23) = \frac{1}{2}(1.23)^3 - \frac{3}{16}(1.23)^4 = 0.501\,27$

Since $P(T \leq 1.22) < 0.5$ and $P(T \leq 1.23) > 0.5$ then $1.22 < m < 1.23$.

(c) $f(t) = \dfrac{d}{dt}F(t)$

Using **4**

$f(t) = \dfrac{d}{dt}(\frac{1}{2}t^3 - \frac{3}{16}t^4)$

So $f(t) = \begin{cases} \frac{3}{2}t^2 - \frac{3}{4}t^3, & 0 \leq t \leq 2, \\ 0, & \text{otherwise.} \end{cases}$

(d) Since $f(0) = f(2) = 0$, the modal time occurs when $\dfrac{d}{dt}f(t) = 0$.

Using **6**

Thus $\qquad \dfrac{d}{dt}(\frac{3}{2}t^2 - \frac{3}{4}t^3) = 3t - \frac{9}{4}t^2 = 0$

i.e. $\qquad\qquad 3t(1 - \frac{3}{4}t) = 0$

i.e. $\qquad\qquad t = 0$ or $t = \frac{4}{3}$

Clearly $t = 0$ is not a sensible solution, so $t = \frac{4}{3}$.

A formal check that this gives a maximum rather than a minimum is not expected in this situation.

(e)

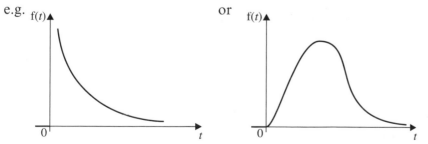

(f) On a windy day there is a greater probability that the value of T is closer to 0.

e.g.

Revision exercise 2

1 Sketch a possible probability density function to model the following continuous random variables.

(a) The number of minutes a randomly selected student has spare at the end of a $1\frac{1}{2}$ hour examination.

(b) The time in seconds it takes an 11 year old child to run 100 m.

2 The continuous random variable X has probability density function

$$f(x) = \begin{cases} \frac{1}{4}(x+2), & -1 \leqslant x \leqslant 1, \\ 0, & \text{otherwise.} \end{cases}$$

(a) Sketch the probability density function.

(b) Write down the mode of X.

(c) Find $E(X)$.

(d) Show that $\text{Var}(X) = \frac{11}{36}$

3 The continuous random variable X has probability density function

$$f(x) = \begin{cases} k(3 + 2x - x^2), & 0 \leqslant x \leqslant 3, \\ 0, & \text{otherwise.} \end{cases}$$

(a) Find k.

(b) Find the mode of X.

4 The continuous random variable X has cumulative distribution function

$$F(x) = \begin{cases} 0, & x < 0, \\ \dfrac{x}{18}(x+3), & 0 \leqslant x \leqslant 3, \\ 1, & x > 3. \end{cases}$$

(a) Find $P(1 < X < 2)$.

(b) Find, to 2 decimal places, the median of X.

(c) Find, to 2 decimal places, the upper and lower quartiles of X.

(d) Comment on the skewness in the light of the calculations in parts (b) and (c).

5 Gill is studying her phone bill. Whenever she rings John the calls last between 2 and 12 minutes. Gill decides to model the duration of a phone call, in minutes, by the random variable T with probability density function

$$f(t) = \begin{cases} \frac{1}{50}(t-2), & 2 \leqslant t \leqslant 12 \\ 0, & \text{otherwise.} \end{cases}$$

(a) Sketch this probability density function.

(b) Show that $E(T) = 8\frac{2}{3}$.

Gill decides to refine her model and uses the random variable S with probability density function

$$g(s) = \begin{cases} c(s-2), & 2 \leqslant s \leqslant 7, \\ c(12-s), & 7 < s \leqslant 12, \\ 0, & \text{otherwise} \end{cases}$$

where c is a constant and a sketch of $g(s)$ is given below.

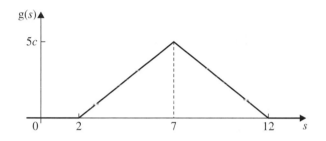

(c) Find the value of c.

(d) Write down $E(S)$.

(e) Give a possible reason why the random variable S may provide a better model than T for the duration of the telephone calls.

6 The continuous random variable T has probability density function $f(x)$ given by

$$f(x) = \begin{cases} 2(x-1), & 1 \leqslant x \leqslant 2, \\ 0, & \text{otherwise.} \end{cases}$$

(a) Show that $E(X) = \frac{5}{3}$.

(b) Find the cumulative distribution function $F(x)$.

(c) Show that the median of X is 1.71 to 3 significant figures.

(d) Write down the mode of X.

(e) Comment on the skewness of the distribution.

Test yourself	What to review

If your answer is incorrect:

1 A horticultural firm is studying the number of hours that daffodils will last in a vase of water with a new additive. The random variable X (in hundreds of hours) with probability density function

$$f(x) = \begin{cases} k(4 - x^2), & 0 \leqslant x \leqslant 2, \\ 0, & \text{otherwise.} \end{cases}$$

is proposed as a model.

(a) Show that $k = \frac{3}{16}$.

(b) Find the mean number of hours that a daffodil will last, according to this model.

(c) Use this model to find the probability that a daffodil will last for more than 100 hours.

The new additive is tested on carnations and it is found that several of these last for over 250 hours.

(d) Explain why the random variable X, with probability density function f(x) as defined above, would not be a suitable model in this case.

(e) Suggest how the probability density function could be changed to model the time carnations will last. [E]

Review Heinemann Book S2 pages 38–42 and 47–52

2 A student observes vehicles passing a particular point. He models the time, in s, between consecutive vehicles by the random variable T. He suggests that a possible cumulative distribution function for T is

$$F(t) = \begin{cases} 0, & t < 0, \\ \dfrac{20t - t^2}{100}, & 0 \leqslant t \leqslant 10, \\ 1, & t > 10. \end{cases}$$

(a) Find the probability that the time between two consecutive vehicles passing the point is less than 7 s but more than 5 s.

(b) Find the probability density function f(t) for T.

(c) Sketch the graph of f(t).

(d) Write down a limitation of this model.

(e) Sketch a possible alternative probability density function for T. [E]

Review Heinemann Book S2 pages 43–47

3 The total number of radio taxi calls received at a control centre in a month is modelled by a random variable X (in tens of thousands of calls) having probability density function

$$f(x) = \begin{cases} cx, & 0 < x < 1, \\ c(2-x), & 1 \leqslant x < 2, \\ 0, & \text{otherwise.} \end{cases}$$

Review Heinemann Book S2 pages 43–47

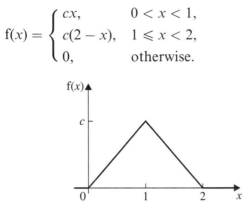

(a) Show that the value of c is 1.

(b) Write down the probability that $X \leqslant 1$.

(c) Show that the cumulative distribution function of X is

$$F(x) = \begin{cases} 0, & x < 0, \\ \frac{1}{2}x^2, & 0 \leqslant x < 1, \\ 2x - \frac{1}{2}x^2 - 1, & 1 \leqslant x < 2, \\ 1, & x \geqslant 2. \end{cases}$$

(d) Find the probability that the control centre receives between 8000 and 12 000 calls in a month.

A colleague criticises this model on the grounds that the number of radio calls must be discrete, while the model for X is continuous.

(e) State briefly whether you consider that it was reasonable to use this model for X.

(f) Give two reasons why the probability density function shown in the diagram might be unsuitable as a model.

(g) Sketch the shape of a more suitable probability density function. [E]

4 The continuous random variable X has a probability density function $f(x)$ given by

$$f(x) = \begin{cases} \frac{1}{8}(2+x) & -2 \leqslant x \leqslant 0, \\ \frac{1}{8}(2-x) & 0 < x \leqslant 2, \\ 0 & \text{otherwise.} \end{cases}$$

Review Heinemann Book S2 pages 47–50

(a) Calculate $E(X)$ and $E(X^2)$.

(b) Write down the mode of X and $Var(X)$.

5 A continuous random variable X has a cumulative
distribution function $F(x)$ given by

Review Heinemann Book S2
pages 47–57

$$F(x) = \begin{cases} 0 & x < 0, \\ \dfrac{x}{8}(x+2) & 0 \leqslant x \leqslant 2, \\ 1 & x > 2. \end{cases}$$

Calculate:
(a) the median of X,
(b) the upper and lower quartiles of X.

Test yourself answers

1 (b) 75 (c) $\frac{5}{16}$ (d) Range < 200 hours (e) Extend range to say 300 hours but certainly more than 250 hours.

2 (a) 0.16 (b) $f(t) = \begin{cases} \frac{1}{50}(10 - t), & 0 \leqslant t \leqslant 10, \\ 0, & \text{otherwise.} \end{cases}$ (c)

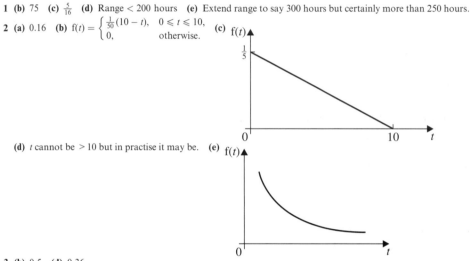

(d) t cannot be > 10 but in practise it may be. (e)

3 (b) 0.5 (d) 0.36
(e) Since X is in tens of thousands it is probably a reasonable approximation. (f) e.g. never get more than 20 000 calls; symmetrical distribution unlikely; distribution is likely to vary with the time of year.
(g)

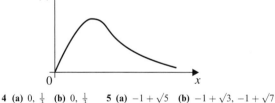

4 (a) 0, $\frac{1}{3}$ (b) 0, $\frac{1}{3}$ 5 (a) $-1 + \sqrt{5}$ (b) $-1 + \sqrt{3}, -1 + \sqrt{7}$

Continuous distributions

3

Key points to remember

1 **Continuous uniform distribution** – often known as the **Rectangular distribution**.
A random variable X, having a continuous uniform distribution over the interval (α, β) has probability density function

$$f(x) = \begin{cases} \dfrac{1}{\beta - \alpha}, & \alpha < x < \beta, \\ 0, & \text{otherwise.} \end{cases}$$

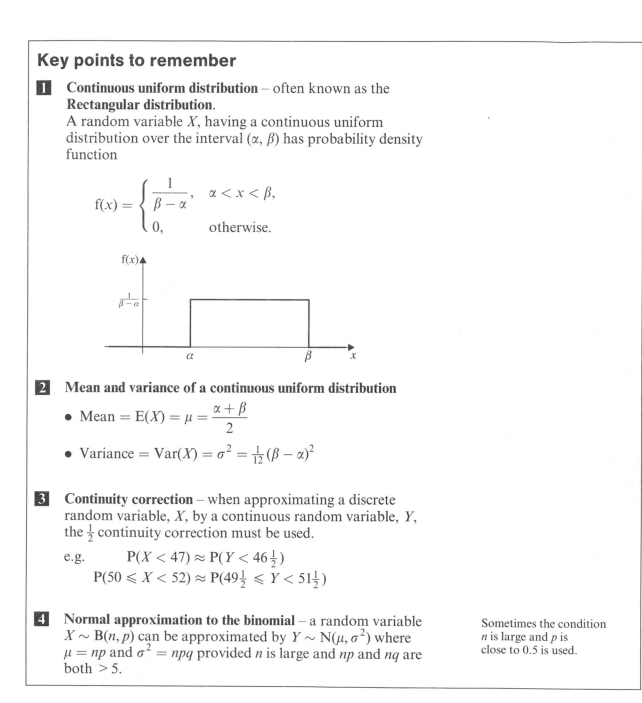

2 **Mean and variance of a continuous uniform distribution**

- Mean $= E(X) = \mu = \dfrac{\alpha + \beta}{2}$

- Variance $= \text{Var}(X) = \sigma^2 = \frac{1}{12}(\beta - \alpha)^2$

3 **Continuity correction** – when approximating a discrete random variable, X, by a continuous random variable, Y, the $\frac{1}{2}$ continuity correction must be used.

e.g. $\quad P(X < 47) \approx P(Y < 46\frac{1}{2})$

$\quad P(50 \leqslant X < 52) \approx P(49\frac{1}{2} \leqslant Y < 51\frac{1}{2})$

4 **Normal approximation to the binomial** – a random variable $X \sim B(n, p)$ can be approximated by $Y \sim N(\mu, \sigma^2)$ where $\mu = np$ and $\sigma^2 = npq$ provided n is large and np and nq are both > 5.

Sometimes the condition n is large and p is close to 0.5 is used.

> **5** **Normal approximation to the Poisson distribution** – a random variable $X \sim \text{Po}(\lambda)$ can be approximated by $Y \sim \text{N}(\lambda, \lambda)$ for $\lambda > 10$.
> The condition $\lambda > 10$ is due to the fact that in the Edexcel tables for the Poisson distribution λ is not tabulated for values > 10.
> For $\lambda < 10$ the normal approximation to the Poisson distribution is poor, but the approximation is much better for larger values of λ, e.g. $\lambda \geqslant 25$.

Example 1

The random variable X is a continuous uniform random variable on the interval $[-4, 6]$.
Find:
(a) $\text{P}(X < -2.5)$
(b) $\text{P}(|X| < 1.3)$
(c) $\text{E}(X)$
(d) $\text{Var}(X)$

Answer

(a) $\text{P}(X < -2.5) = 1.5 \times \frac{1}{10} = 0.15$ Using **1**

(b) $\text{P}(|X| < 1.3) = 2 \times 1.3 \times \frac{1}{10} = 0.26$ Using **1**

(c) $\text{E}(X) = \dfrac{6-4}{2} = 1$ Using **2**

(d) $\text{Var}(X) = \frac{1}{12}(6+4)^2 = \frac{100}{12} = 8\frac{1}{3}$ Using **2**

Try answering parts **(a)** and **(b)** from first principles using integration and by sketching the probability density function of X and using your knowledge of geometry.

Example 2

The random variable $X \sim \text{B}(100, 0.45)$. Using a suitable approximation find $\text{P}(35 < X \leqslant 46)$.

Answer

Since n is large, p is close to 0.5, $np = 45$ and $nq = 55$ (i.e. both greater than 5) you need to use the normal approximation to the binomial distribution with $\mu = np$ and $\sigma^2 = npq$.
In this case $np = 45$ and $npq = 24.75$.
Using **3** and **4**,

$$\text{P}(35 < X \leqslant 46) \approx \text{P}(35.5 < Y \leqslant 46.5) \qquad \text{where } Y \sim \text{N}(45, 24.75)$$

$$= \text{P}\left(\frac{35.5 - 45}{\sqrt{24.75}} < Z \leqslant \frac{46.5 - 45}{\sqrt{24.75}}\right)$$

$$= \text{P}(-1.91 < Z \leqslant 0.30)$$

$$= \Phi(0.30) - [1 - \Phi(1.91)]$$

$$= 0.6179 + 0.9719 - 1$$

$$= 0.5898$$

> Remember to use the standard deviation in the denominator when standardising. Hence $\sqrt{24.75}$ in this example. As for S1, standardise to 2 decimal places.

If you interpolate or use a calculator you get a slightly different answer. For example, the calculator gives 0.5904 (4 d.p.) rather than 0.5898. In the examination answers from the tables using two decimal places, interpolation or the calculator are all acceptable.

Example 3

A factory produces screws of which 4% are defective.
(a) Find the probability that in a packet of 10 screws fewer than 3 are defective.
(b) Using a suitable approximation, find the probability that a box of 300 screws will contain at least 9 but fewer than 14 defective screws.

Answer

(a) Let X represent the number of defective screws.
$\therefore\quad X \sim B(10, 0.04)$

Using Chapter 1,

$$P(X < 3) = P(X \leqslant 2) = 0.9938$$

(b) Since n is large (300) and p is small (0.04) you may initially think of using the Poisson approximation to the binomial distribution with $\lambda = np = 300 \times 0.04 = 12$. Unfortunately the Edexcel Poisson distribution tables stop at $\lambda = 10$ and so you will need to use the normal approximation with $np = 12$ and $npq = 11.52$. (Note that $np = 12$ and $nq = 288$ are both greater than 5.)

> This is not the most effective use of the normal approximation to the binomial distribution. This happens when $p = \frac{1}{2}$. Thus the closer p is to $\frac{1}{2}$ the better the approximation.

Using **3** and **4**,

$$P(9 \leqslant X < 14) \approx P(8.5 \leqslant Y < 13.5) \text{ where } Y \sim N(12, 11.52)$$
$$= P(-1.03 \leqslant Z < 0.44)$$
$$= \Phi(0.44) + \Phi(1.03) - 1$$
$$= 0.5185$$

> Again interpolation and calculator give slightly different answers.

Example 4

The random variable $X \sim Po(32)$.
Use a suitable approximation to find $P(X = 26)$.

Answer

Use the normal approximation to the Poisson distribution with $\mu = \lambda$ and $\sigma^2 = \lambda$.

$$P(X = 26) \approx P(25.5 \leqslant Y \leqslant 26.5) \text{ where } Y \sim N(32, 32)$$
$$= P(-1.15 \leqslant Z \leqslant -0.97)$$
$$= \Phi(-0.97) - \Phi(-1.15)$$
$$= 1 - \Phi(0.97) - 1 + \Phi(1.15)$$
$$= 0.8749 - 0.8340$$
$$= 0.0409$$

> Using **3** and **5**

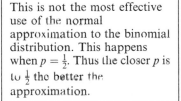

Example 5

Breakdowns occur on a stretch of road at random and at a rate of 5.6 per week.

(a) Find the probability that in a particular week more than 2 breakdowns occur.

(b) Using a normal approximation estimate the probability that in a 12-week period fewer than 55 breakdowns occur.

Answer

(a) Let B represent the number of breakdowns in a week.

$\therefore \quad B \sim \text{Po}(5.6)$

$$P(B > 2) = P(B \geqslant 3) = 1 - P(B \leqslant 2)$$

$$= 1 - e^{-5.6}\left\{1 + 5.6 + \frac{(5.6)^2}{2!}\right\}$$

 Using **3** from Chapter 1B

$$= 0.9176$$

(b) Let X represent the number of breakdowns per 12-week period.

$\therefore \quad X \sim \text{Po}(12 \times 5.6 = 67.2)$

Using **3** and **5**,

$$P(X < 55) \approx P(Y < 54.5) \text{ where } Y \sim \text{N}(67.2, 67.2)$$

$$= P\left(Z \leqslant \frac{54.5 - 67.2}{\sqrt{67.2}}\right)$$

$$= P(Z \leqslant -1.55)$$

$$= 1 - \Phi(1.55)$$

$$= 0.0606$$

Worked examination question 1[E]

A child has a pair of scissors and a piece of string 8 cm long, which has a mark on one end. The child cuts the string, at a randomly chosen point, into two pieces. Let X represent the length of the piece of string with the mark on it.

(a) Suggest a suitable model for the distribution of X.

(b) Sketch the probability density function associated with your model.

(c) Using your model, evaluate the probability that the shorter piece of string is at least 3 cm long.

Answer

(a) A continuous uniform (or rectangular) distribution on the interval $(0, 8)$.

Using **1**

(b)

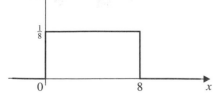

(c) P(shorter piece of string $\geqslant 3\,\text{cm}$) $= \text{P}(3 < X < 4) + \text{P}(4 < X < 5)$

$$= \text{P}(3 < X < 5)$$
$$= \tfrac{1}{8}(5 - 3)$$
$$= \tfrac{1}{4}$$

Worked examination question 2[E]

Articles are produced by independent operations of a machine. The probability that any one article is acceptable is θ.

As the articles are produced they are placed at random in small boxes, each box containing five articles.

(a) Show that the probability that a small box contains more acceptable articles than unacceptable ones is given by $\theta^3(10 - 15\theta + 6\theta^2)$.

(b) Find the probability that the last article placed in a small box is the second unacceptable article in that box.

A large box contains 150 randomly selected articles.

(c) Assuming that $\theta = 0.85$ and using a suitable approximation, find the probability that this box contains at least 135 acceptable articles.

Answer

(a) Let X represent the number of acceptable articles in a box.

$\therefore \quad X \sim \text{B}(5, \theta)$

$$\text{P}(X \geqslant 3) = \text{P}(X = 3) + \text{P}(X = 4) + \text{P}(X = 5)$$

Using Chapter 1A

$$= {}^5\text{C}_3\theta^3(1 - \theta)^2 + {}^5\text{C}_4\theta^4(1 - \theta) + \theta^5$$
$$= 10\theta^3(1 - \theta)^2 + 5\theta^4(1 - \theta) + \theta^5$$
$$= \theta^3[10(1 - \theta)^2 + 5\theta(1 - \theta) + \theta^2]$$
$$= \theta^3(10 + 10\theta^2 - 20\theta + 5\theta - 5\theta^2 + \theta^2)$$
$$= \theta^3(10 - 15\theta + 6\theta^2)$$

(b) P(last is 2nd unacceptable) $= \text{P}(3 \text{ acceptable in 1st four}) \times \text{P}(\text{unacceptable})$

$$= {}^4\text{C}_3\theta^3(1 - \theta) \times (1 - \theta)$$
$$= 4\theta^3(1 - \theta)^2$$

(c) Let A represent the number of acceptable articles in a box of 150.

$\therefore \quad A \sim \text{B}(150, 0.85)$

Using **3** and **4** with $\quad \mu = 150 \times 0.85 = 127.5$

and $\quad \sigma^2 = 150 \times 0.85 \times 0.15 = 19.125$

$$\text{P}(A \geqslant 135) \approx \text{P}(Y \geqslant 134.5) \text{ where } Y \sim \text{N}(127.5, 19.125)$$
$$= \text{P}\!\left(Z \geqslant \frac{134.5 - 127.5}{\sqrt{19.125}}\right)$$
$$= \text{P}(Z \geqslant 1.60)$$
$$= 0.0548$$

Worked examination question 3[E]

Frugal bakeries claim that packs of 10 of their buns contain on average 75 raisins. A Poisson distribution is used to model the number of raisins in a randomly selected bun.
(a) Specify the value of the parameter.
(b) State any assumption required about the distribution of raisins in the production process for this model to be valid.
(c) Show that the probability that a randomly selected bun contains more than 8 raisins is 0.338.
(d) Find the probability that in a pack of 10 buns at least two buns contain more than 8 raisins.
(e) Using a suitable approximation, find the probability that in a pack of 10 buns there are more than 80 raisins.

Answer

(a) $\lambda = \frac{75}{10} = 7.5$

(b) Raisins must be randomly scattered.

(c) Let X represent the number of raisins in a bun.
$\therefore \quad X \sim \text{Po}(7.5)$
Using Chapter 1,

$$\begin{aligned}
P(X > 8) &= 1 - P(X \leqslant 8) \\
&= 1 - 0.6620 \\
&= 0.338
\end{aligned}$$

(d) Let Y represent the number of buns with more than 8 raisins.
$\therefore \quad Y \sim \text{B}(10, 0.338)$.
Using Chapter 1,

$$\begin{aligned}
P(Y \geqslant 2) &= 1 - P(Y \leqslant 1) \\
&= 1 - [P(Y = 0) + P(Y = 1)] \\
&= 1 - [(0.662)^{10} + 10(0.662)^9(0.338)] \\
&= 0.9013
\end{aligned}$$

(e) Let R represent the number of raisins in 10 buns.
$\therefore \quad R \sim \text{Po}(\lambda = 75)$
Using **3** and **5**,

$$\begin{aligned}
P(R > 80) &\approx P(Y > 80.5) \text{ where } Y \sim N(75, 75) \\
&= P\left(Z > \frac{80.5 - 75}{\sqrt{75}}\right) \\
&= P(Z > 0.635) \\
&= 0.2627
\end{aligned}$$

Note that the value of Z has been left to 3 decimal places since rounding to 2 decimal places might have resulted in 0.63 or 0.64. Interpolation is easy in such a situation. In the examination a range would be given for the final answer and any value in that range would gain the mark.

Revision exercise 3

1 The random variable X is a continuous uniform random variable on the interval $(-8, -1)$.
Find:
(a) $P(X > -3)$
(b) $E(X - 4)$
(c) $Var(2X + 3)$

2 The random variable $Y \sim B(90, 0.42)$.
Using a suitable approximation find $P(33 \leqslant Y < 42)$.

3 The probability that it rains in Dampsville on any given day independently of any other day is 0.4.
(a) Find the probability that in any 7-day week it rains on exactly 4 days.
(b) Using a suitable approximation find the probability that in a 90-day period it rains on fewer than 30 days.
(c) Comment on the assumption of independence.

4 The random variable $X \sim Po(36)$.
Using a suitable approximation find $P(X = 40)$.

5 A biologist is studying the behaviour of sheep in a large field. The field is divided into a number of equally sized squares and the average number of sheep per square is 2.5. The sheep are randomly spread throughout the field.
(a) Suggest a suitable model for the number of sheep in a square and give a suitable value for any parameter or parameters required.

Calculate the probability that a randomly selected square contains
(b) no sheep,
(c) more than 4 sheep.

A sheep dog has been sent into the field to round up the sheep.
(d) Explain why the model may no longer be applicable.

In another field the average number of sheep per square is 20 and the sheep are scattered randomly throughout the field.
(e) Using a suitable approximation, find the probability that a randomly selected square contains fewer than 15 sheep.   [E]

6 Faults occur in cable at random and at a rate of 0.027 per metre.

(a) Find the probability that in a 20-metre length of cable there will be no faults.

(b) Using a normal approximation, estimate the probability that in a 1 km length of cable there will be more than 33 faults.

Test yourself	What to review

If your answer is incorrect:

1 The random variable X is a continuous uniform random variable on the interval $(2, \beta)$.
(a) Given that $P(X > 5) = 0.625$ find β.
(b) Find $E(X)$ and $Var(X)$.
(c) Find $P(X \geqslant E(X) - 2)$.

Review Heinemann Book S2 pages 71–76

2 Of the bolts produced by a factory, 5% are defective.
(a) Find the probability that in a box of 20 bolts more than 3 are defective.
(b) Using a normal approximation find the probability that in a box of 250 bolts there will be between 10 and 14 (inclusive) defective.

Review Heinemann Book S2 pages 76–79

3 A particular make of kettle is sold by a shop at an average rate of 5 per week. The random variable X represents the number of kettles sold in any one week and X is modelled by a Poisson distribution.
The shop manager notices that at the beginning of a particular week there are 7 kettles in stock.
(a) Find the probability that the shop will not be able to meet all the demands for kettles that week, assuming that it is not possible to restock during the week.

In order to increase sales performance, the manager decides to have in stock at the beginning of each week sufficient kettles to have at least a 99% chance of being able to meet all demands during that week.
(b) Find the smallest number of kettles that should be in stock at the beginning of each week.
(c) Using a suitable approximation find the probability that the shop sells at least 18 kettles in a 4-week period, subject to stock always being available to meet demand.

Review Heinemann Book S2 pages 79–83

Test yourself answers

1 (a) 10 **(b)** 6, $\frac{16}{3}$ **(c)** $\frac{3}{4}$ **2 (a)** 0.0159 **(b)** 0.527 **3 (a)** 0.133 **(b)** 11 **(c)** 0.712

Hypothesis tests

Key points to remember

1 **Population** – a collection of items.

2 **Sampling frame** – a list of items in a population.

3 **Census** – a complete enumeration of a population.

4 **Sample** – a selection of items from a population.

5 **Statistic** – a random variable consisting of any function of the sample data that involves no other quantities.

6 **Null hypothesis** (H_0) – the working hypothesis, which is assumed to be true.

A hypothesis test about a population parameter θ is always stated in terms of θ.

7 **Alternative hypothesis** (H_1) – the hypothesis that describes the situation if H_0 is not true.

H_1 indicates whether the test is one-tailed or two-tailed.

8 **Test statistic** – a statistic used in a hypothesis test.

9 **Sampling distribution** – the distribution of a statistic.

In S2 this should be binomial or Poisson for hypothesis tests.

10 **Critical region** – the range of values of a test statistic that would lead you to reject H_0.

11 **Significance level** – used to determine the critical region. It is the level of probability we are prepared to accept. It is the probability of rejecting H_0 assuming H_0 is true.

Remember for tests involving discrete distributions the actual significance level will often be different from the intended one.

Example 1

Suggest a suitable statistic and an appropriate sampling distribution in the following situations. In each case state suitable null and alternative hypotheses.

(a) To test whether or not a coin is biased if it is tossed 10 times.

(b) A secretary usually makes errors at the rate of 1.5 per page. On a Friday afternoon at the end of a busy week he types a 5-page report. The secretary's boss wishes to know whether or not the secretary has been less careful than usual.

Answer
(a) $X =$ the number of times the coin lands heads

$X \sim B(10, p)$

$H_0: p = 0.5$ $\qquad\qquad$ $H_1: p \neq 0.5$

(b) $X =$ the number of errors on a 5-page report

$X \sim Po(5 \times \lambda)$ where $\lambda =$ average number of errors per page.

$H_0: \lambda = 1.5$ $\qquad\qquad$ $H_1: \lambda > 1.5$

(Rate of errors is the same) $\quad$ (Rate of errors has increased)

Example 2
Find the critical region for the test statistic $X \sim B(10, p)$ where the null hypothesis is $H_0: p = 0.35$ and the alternative hypothesis is $H_1: p \neq 0.35$. Use a 5% level of significance and choose the critical value so that the probability of rejection in each tail is as close as possible to 2.5%.

Answer
$P(X \leqslant 1) = 0.0860$

$P(X \leqslant 0) = 0.0135$

So the lower critical value is 0.

$\boxed{\text{Using tables}}$

$P(X \geqslant 7) = 1 - P(X \leqslant 6) = 1 - 0.9740 = 0.0260$

$P(X \geqslant 8) = 1 - P(X \leqslant 7) = 1 - 0.9952 = 0.0048$

So the upper critical value is 7.

Therefore the critical region is $X = 0$ or $X \geqslant 7$.

Example 3
(a) Use a 5% significance level to find a critical region for the test statistic $X \sim Po(\lambda)$ with the hypotheses $H_0: \lambda = 4.5$ and $H_1: \lambda > 4.5$.

(b) State the probability of rejection for this critical region.

Answer
(a) $P(X \geqslant 9) = 1 - P(X \leqslant 8) = 1 - 0.9597 = 0.0403$

$\qquad\;\; P(X \geqslant 10) = 1 - P(X \leqslant 9) = 1 - 0.9829 = 0.0171$

So the critical region is $X \geqslant 9$.

(b) The probability of rejection is $P(X \geqslant 9) = 0.0403$.

$\boxed{\text{Closest to 5\%}}$

Example 4
The probability that Bhavna scores from a penalty flick in a game of hockey is 0.75.

Before an important cup match she spends an afternoon practising with her coach. In the warm-up before the match Bhavna takes 10 practice penalty flicks and scores with 9 of them.

Determine whether or not there is evidence that the coaching has helped Bhavna improve. State your hypotheses clearly and use a 5% level of significance.

Answer

Let $X =$ the number of goals Bhavna scores from 10 penalty flicks.

We assume that the coaching makes no difference (i.e. H_0: $p = 0.75$) and then

$$X \sim B(10, 0.75)$$

Since the tables only have values of p up to 0.5 we use the random variable Y where $Y =$ the number of times Bhavna *misses* from 10 penalty flicks.

Under H_0, $Y \sim B(10, 0.25)$.
The solution proceeds as follows:

$$H_0: p = 0.75 \ (or \ 0.25) \qquad H_1: p > 0.75 \ (or < 0.25)$$

Observed value for Y is $y = 1$ and from tables $P(Y \leqslant 1) = 0.2440$. This is greater than 5% so there is insufficient evidence to reject H_0 and we conclude that there is not sufficient evidence to say that the coaching has led to an improvement.

> Always state your conclusion in terms of the context.

Worked examination question 1[E]

A manufacturer of windows has used a process that produced random flaws in the glass at a rate of 0.5 per m². In an attempt to reduce the number of flaws produced, a new process is tried out. A randomly chosen window produced using this new process has an area of 8 m² and contains only 1 flaw.

Stating your hypotheses clearly, test at the 10% level of significance whether or not the rate of occurrence of flaws using this new procedure has decreased.

Answer

$$H_0: \lambda = 0.5 \text{ per m}^2$$
$$H_1: \lambda < 0.5 \text{ per m}^2$$

> If the process works it should lead to a decrease in the rate of flaws.

Let $X =$ the number of flaws in 8 m². Under H_0, $X \sim Po(4)$

> $\lambda = 8 \times 0.5$

$$P(X \leqslant 1) = 0.0916$$

> Observed $x = 1$

This is less than 10% so the result is significant and we have evidence to reject H_0 and conclude that the new process has been successful.

> State your conclusions in terms of context.

Worked examination question 2[E]

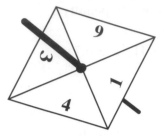

A square spinner for use in a child's game has four numbers 1, 3, 4 and 6 on its edges as shown. The manufacturer claims that the probability that the spinner lands on each of the four numbers is $\frac{1}{4}$. Before a box of spinners leaves the factory a randomly chosen spinner is tested by spinning it 20 times and recording the number of sixes.

(a) Using a 5% significance level, find the critical regions for a two-tailed test of the hypothesis that the probability of a spinner landing on a six is $\frac{1}{4}$.

(b) Explain how a spinner could pass this test but still not satisfy the manufacturer's claim.

Answer

$H_0: p = \frac{1}{4}$ $H_1: p \neq \frac{1}{4}$

(a) Let $X =$ the number of times the spinner lands on a six in 20 spins.

Under H_0, $X \sim B(20, \frac{1}{4})$

$P(X \leqslant 1) = 0.0243$

$P(X \leqslant 2) = 0.0913$

> Using tables

So the lower critical value is 1.

$P(X \geqslant 9) = 1 - P(X \leqslant 8) = 1 - 0.9591 = 0.0409$

$P(X \geqslant 10) = 1 - P(X \leqslant 9) = 1 - 0.9861 = 0.0139$

> Closest to 0.025

So the upper critical value is 10.

Therefore the critical region is $\{X \leqslant 1\} \cup \{X \geqslant 10\}$

(b) Could have $P(6) = \frac{1}{4}$ but the others different, e.g. $P(3) = \frac{1}{2}$

Revision exercise 4

1 A bowling club has 238 members. The committee would like to know what the members' views are about the facilities offered by the club.

(a) State, giving a reason, whether the committee should take a sample or a census.

(b) Suggest a possible sampling frame.

2 A coin is tossed 10 times and lands heads on 7 occasions.
  (a) Stating your hypotheses clearly, test at the 5% level of significance whether or not there is evidence that the coin is biased.
  (b) Find critical regions to test whether or not the coin is biased, based on 20 tosses. The probability of rejection in each tail should be as close as possible to 2.5%.

3 On Wednesday afternoons last year a teacher regularly took her class out to study traffic flow through a small village. Her studies established that lorries pass through the village at a rate of 1.5 per 5-minute period on Wednesday afternoons.

  This year she had to take the class out on Thursday morning. In a half-hour period the class observed 15 lorries passing through the village.

  Stating your hypotheses clearly and using a 5% level of significance, test whether or not there is evidence that the rate of lorries passing through on Thursday mornings is greater than the rate on Wednesday afternoons.

4 An official of the Department of Transport was studying the distribution of the number of vehicles in a queue at a set of temporary traffic lights. She modelled the number of vehicles as a Poisson random variable. She wished to test the null hypothesis that the parameter was 7 against the alternative hypothesis that it was greater than 7. She intended to make one observation, and decided that the critical region would be 12 or greater.
  (a) Determine the actual significance level of this test.

  She later changed her mind and decided that her alternative hypothesis should be that the parameter was not equal to 7. She decided to take the largest critical region for which the probability in each 'tail' was less than 2.5%.
  (b) Find the critical region which she should choose.
  (c) Determine the actual significance level she would be using with this critical region. [E]

5 A large college introduced a new procedure to try and ensure that staff arrived on time for the start of lectures. A recent survey by the students had suggested that in 15% of cases the staff arrived late for the start of a lecture. In the first week following the introduction of this new procedure a random sample of 35 lectures was taken and in only 1 case did the member of staff arrive late.

(a) Stating your hypotheses clearly test, at the 5% level of significance, whether or not there is evidence that the new procedure has been successful.

A student complained that this sample did not give a true picture of the effectiveness of the new procedure.

(b) Explain briefly why the student's claim might be justified and suggest how a more effective check on the new procedure could be made.   [E]

Test yourself	What to review

If your answer is incorrect:

1 The committee of a squash club asked a random sample of 50 members whether or not they were in favour of a scheme to spend club funds on installing a sauna. The members were each sent a form and asked to vote yes or no for the scheme.

(a) Suggest a suitable sampling frame.
(b) Define a statistic that might be connected with this sample survey.
(c) Give the sampling distribution of your statistic.

The committee will only go ahead with the scheme if they have evidence that at least $\frac{2}{3}$ of the members are in favour. They propose to carry out a suitable statistical test, using the results of the survey, to decide the matter.

(d) State suitable null and alternative hypotheses.
(e) Explain how you would find a critical region for this test using a 5% level of significance.

[You are *not* expected to calculate this critical region.]

Review Heinemann Book S2 pages 85–99

2 Some children are playing with a cubical die. They have rolled the die 12 times but have not obtained a single six.
(a) Stating your hypotheses clearly, test at the 10% level of significance, whether or not there is evidence that the probability of throwing a six on this die is less than $\frac{1}{6}$.

On another occasion the children rolled the die 25 times and only obtained 1 six.
(b) Determine whether or not this experiment gives evidence, at the 10% level of significance, that the probability of throwing a six is less than $\frac{1}{6}$.

Review Heinemann Book S2 pages 96–104

3 A manufacturer of rope knows that tangles in the threads occur at a rate of 0.8 per metre. In order to monitor the process, every hour the manufacturer examines a 5 m length of rope from the production line to test whether or not the rate of occurrence of tangles has increased.
(a) Stating your hypotheses clearly and using a significance level as close as possible to 5%, determine the critical region for this test.

The manufacturer has just examined a 5 m length of rope and discovered 7 tangles in the thread.
(b) Explain what the manufacturer's reaction should be.

Review Heinemann Book S2 pages 105–106

4 A statistician is hanging out the washing with coloured pegs. Each peg is selected at random from a large bag and 20% of the pegs are supposed to be blue. The statistician notices that only 1 of the last 20 pegs he has selected from the bag is blue.
(a) Stating your hypotheses clearly test, using a 5% level of significance, whether or not there is evidence that the proportion of blue pegs in the bag is less than 20%.

The proportion of red pegs in the bag is supposed to be 30%. A random sample of 20 pegs is examined.
(b) Find the critical region for a two-tailed test of this hypothesis. You should ensure that the probability for each 'tail' is as close as possible to 2.5%.
(c) State the actual significance level for the test defined in part **(b)**.

Review Heinemann Book S2 pages 97–106

Test yourself answers

1 (a) List of club members. **(b)** X = the number of members who vote yes. **(c)** $X \sim$ Binomial, $n = 50$, p to be determined.
(d) $H_0: p = \frac{2}{3}$ $H_1: p > \frac{2}{3}$ **(e)** Find c such that $P(X \geq c | X \sim B(50, \frac{2}{3}))$ is close to 0.05.
2 (a) $H_0: p = \frac{1}{6}$ $H_1: p < \frac{1}{6}$. $P(X = 0) = 0.112\ldots > 10\%$ so not significant. Insufficient evidence to suspect the probability is less than $\frac{1}{6}$.
(b) $P(X \leq 1) = 0.0629 < 10\%$. There is evidence that the probability is less than $\frac{1}{6}$.
3 (a) $H_0: \lambda = 4$ $H_1: \lambda > 4$; Critical region $X \geq 8$ **(b)** Not significant. Insufficient evidence of an increase, not concerned.
4 (a) $H_0: p = 0.2$ $H_1: p < 0.2$. $P(X \leq 1) = 0.0692 > 5\%$ so not significant. Insufficient evidence to say that p is less than 20%.
(b) $H_0: p = 0.3$ $H_1: p \neq 0.3$. Critical region is $Y \leq 2$ or $Y \geq 11$. **(c)** Significance level is 0.0526

Examination style paper

Attempt **all** questions   **Time 90 minutes**

In calculations you are advised to show all the steps in your working, giving your answer at each stage. Critical values from the Statistical Tables should be **quoted in full**. The answer to each part of a question which requires the use of tables or a calculator should be given to an appropriate degree of accuracy.

1. (*a*) The random variable $X \sim B(10, 0.35)$.
   Find $P(X \leqslant 4)$.
   (*b*) The random variable Y has a Poisson distribution with mean 7.5.
   Find $P(Y > 7)$.
   (*c*) The random variable $Z \sim N(0, 1)$.
   Find $P(|Z| > 1.29)$.

                                                           (5 marks)

2. The manufacturer of a new type of light bulb is concerned to monitor the lifetime of this new bulb. Consequently bulbs are selected at random from the production line and on a test-bed the number of minutes, to the nearest minute, that each bulb lasts is recorded.
   (*a*) Explain why the manufacturer takes a random sample rather than a census.

   The error, in seconds, in measuring the lifetime of a light bulb on this test-bed is represented by the continuous uniform random variable X, where X is distributed over the interval $(-30, 30)$.
   (*b*) Find the probability that the lifetime is overestimated by more than 12 seconds.
   (*c*) Find $P(|X| < 10)$.

   A manager selects a random sample of 5 bulbs and checks their lifetimes on the test-bed.
   (*d*) Find the probability that exactly 2 of the lifetimes are within 10 seconds of their true lifetime.

                                                         (8 marks)

3. A store sells muesli in bags marked 'minimum contents 1 kg'. A student working in the store monitors the actual amount of muesli in the bags and records the difference, in grams, between the actual amount and the minimum amount stated.
   The student suggests that the difference can be modelled by the random variable X having cumulative distribution function

$$F(x) = \begin{cases} 0, & x < 0, \\ \dfrac{28x - x^2}{196}, & 0 \leqslant x \leqslant 14, \\ 1, & x > 14. \end{cases}$$

(a) Find the probability that the difference is greater than 9 g.
(b) Find the probability density function, f(x), of X.
(c) Sketch the graph of f(x).
(d) Write down the limitation of this model.
(e) Sketch a possible alternative. **(9 marks)**

4. A shop sells a particular make of squash racket at a rate of 3 per week. Assuming that sales of this particular racket occur at random, find the probability that:
(a) exactly 4 are sold in a particular week,
(b) at least 8 are sold in a two-week period,
(c) exactly 4 are sold in each of three consecutive weeks.

The shop manager decides to replenish stocks of this racket to a constant level r at the start of each week.
(d) Find the value of r such that, on average, the stock will be insufficient no more than once in a 26-week period. **(10 marks)**

5. A manufacturer of commemorative plates knows from past records that 10% of the production will be flawed. A random sample of 50 plates is checked and the number of flawed plates is recorded.
(a) Using a 5% level of significance, find the critical regions for a two-tailed test of the hypothesis that the probability of a flawed plate is 0.10.
The probability of rejection, in each tail, should be as close to 2.5% as possible.
(b) Write down the actual significance of the above test.

The owner of a souvenir shop knows from past experience that the plates sell at an average rate of 1 per day. In a particular 7-day period the shop sold 13 plates.
(c) Stating your hypotheses clearly, test at the 5% level of significance, whether or not there is evidence that the average number of sales per day has changed during this period.
(11 marks)

6. A pottery produces large quantities of drinking mugs and knows from past experience that 5% of its production will be classified as 'seconds'.
A random sample of 20 mugs is taken from the production.
(a) Write down an appropriate distribution to model the number of 'seconds' in a sample of size 20.
(b) Find the probability that:
    (i) there are exactly 2 'seconds' in the sample,
    (ii) there are more than 4 'seconds' in the sample.

A random sample of size 150 is taken.
(c) Find the probability that the number of 'seconds' in this sample is between 12 and 15 (inclusive), using:
    (i) a Poisson approximation,
    (ii) a normal approximation.
(d) State why an adjustment had to be made when using the normal approximation. **(16 marks)**

7. The random variable X has probability density function

$$f(x) = \begin{cases} \dfrac{k}{3}(x - 2), & 2 < x < 5, \\ \dfrac{k}{3}(8 - x), & 5 \leqslant x < 8, \\ 0, & \text{otherwise} \end{cases}$$

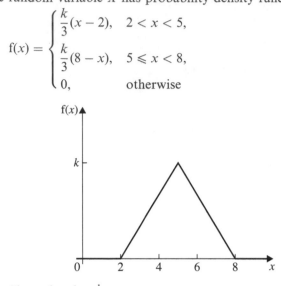

(a) Show that $k = \frac{1}{3}$.

(b) Write down $P(X \leqslant 5)$.

(c) Show that the cumulative distribution function of X is

$$F(x) = \begin{cases} 0, & x < 2, \\ \frac{1}{18}\{x^2 - 4x + 4\}, & 2 \leqslant x < 5, \\ \frac{1}{18}\{16x - x^2 - 46\}, & 5 \leqslant x < 8, \\ 1, & \text{otherwise.} \end{cases}$$

(d) Find $P(4 \leqslant X \leqslant 7)$.

(e) Find the lower quartile of the distribution. **(16 marks)**

Answers

Revision exercise 1A

1 **(a)** 0.3438

 (b) 0.0938

2 **(a)** 0.1715 **(b)** $0.6477 > 0.5$

3 **(a)** $B(20, 0.3)$

 (b) (i) 0.1789 (ii) 0.1133

4 **(a)** $B(20, 0.08)$

 (b) $P(X = 1) = 0.3282$; $P(X = 2) = 0.2711$;
$P(X \geqslant 6) - 0.0038$

 (c) 0.9294

 (d) 0.0706

5 **(a)** 19

 (b) 38.4

Revision exercise 1B

1 **(a)** 0.5488

 (b) 0.0231

2 **(a)** 0.1042 **(b)** 0.0916 **(c)** 0.7619

3 **(a)** 0.4066 **(b)** 0.2275

4 **(a)** $X \sim B(20, 0.2)$

 (b) (i) 0.1369 (ii) 0.3704

 (c) 0.3498

5 **(a)** $Po(1.5)$ **(b)** 0.0186 **(c)** 0.0413

Revision exercise 2

1 A number of other sketches are possible.

 (a)

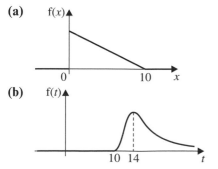

 (b)

2 **(a)**

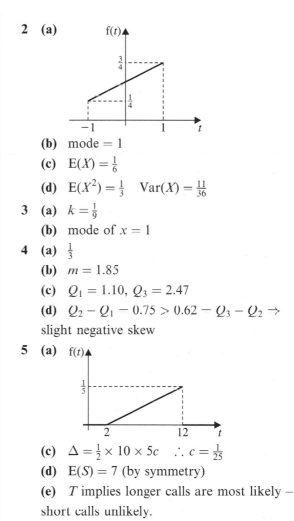

 (b) mode $= 1$

 (c) $E(X) = \frac{1}{6}$

 (d) $E(X^2) = \frac{1}{3}$ $Var(X) = \frac{11}{36}$

3 **(a)** $k = \frac{1}{9}$

 (b) mode of $x = 1$

4 **(a)** $\frac{1}{3}$

 (b) $m = 1.85$

 (c) $Q_1 = 1.10$, $Q_3 = 2.47$

 (d) $Q_2 - Q_1 - 0.75 > 0.62 - Q_3 - Q_2 \rightarrow$
slight negative skew

5 **(a)**

 (c) $\Delta = \frac{1}{2} \times 10 \times 5c$ $\therefore c = \frac{1}{25}$

 (d) $E(S) = 7$ (by symmetry)

 (e) T implies longer calls are most likely –
short calls unlikely.

 S suggests that very short and very long calls
are less likely and most are close to mean.

6 **(b)** $F(x) = \begin{cases} 0 & x < 1, \\ x^2 - 2x + 1 & 1 \leqslant x \leqslant 2, \\ 1 & x > 2. \end{cases}$

 (c) $m = 1.707$

 (d) mode is 2

 (e) $\mu < m < \text{mode} \Rightarrow -\text{ve skew}$

Revision exercise 3

1 (a) $\frac{2}{7}$ (b) -8.5 (c) $\frac{49}{3}$

2 0.656

3 (a) 0.1935

(b) 0.0808

(c) Unlikely that independence holds since rain tends to occur in spells over several consecutive days, rather than at random.

4 0.0544

5 (a) Poisson; 2.5

(b) 0.0821

(c) 0.1088

(d) Sheep no longer randomly scattered

(e) 0.1093

6 (a) 0.583 (b) 0.1056

Revision exercise 4

1 (a) Census – since population is fairly small and this will be more accurate; *or* Sample – since it will be quicker and cheaper (but less reliable)

(b) List of members

2 (a) H_0: $p = 0.5$ H_1: $p \neq 0.5$
$P(\geqslant 7 \mid p = 0.5) = 0.1719 > 0.05$. Not significant. Insufficient evidence to reject H_0, no reason to suspect coin of bias.

(b) $\{Y \leqslant 5\} \cup \{Y \geqslant 15\}$

3 H_0: $\lambda = 9$ H_1: $\lambda > 9$ Significant.
$P(\geqslant 15 \mid \lambda = 9) = 0.0415 < 0.05$. Reject H_0.
There is evidence that the rate of lorries is greater on Thursday mornings.

4 (a) 0.0533 (b) $\{X \leqslant 1\} \cup \{X \geqslant 14\}$

(c) Significance level $= 0.0201$

5 (a) H_0: $p = 0.15$, H_1: $p < 0.15$
$P(\leqslant 1 \mid p = 0.15) = 0.0243 < 0.05$. There is evidence that the new procedure has been working.

(b) Sample taken over a single week. Better to take a random sample over a number of weeks.

Examination style paper

1 (a) 0.7515

(b) 0.4754

(c) 0.1970

2 (a) A census involves using every element in the population and to use a census in this case would destroy all the production.

(b) 0.3 (c) $\frac{1}{3}$ (d) $\frac{80}{243}$

3 (a) $\frac{25}{196}$

(b) $f(x) = \frac{1}{98}(14 - x)$, $0 \leqslant x \leqslant 14$

(c)

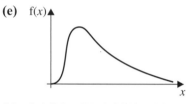

(d) x cannot be greater than 14, but in practice it could be.

(e)

4 (a) 0.1681 (b) 0.2560 (c) 0.004 75

(d) 6

5 (a) $X \leqslant 1$ or $X \geqslant 9$

(b) 0.0583

(c) H_0: $\lambda = 7$, H_1: $\lambda \neq 7$
$P(Y \geqslant 13) = 0.0270 > 0.025 \Rightarrow$ insufficient evidence of change.

6 (a) $X \sim B(20, 0.05)$

(b) (i) 0.1887 (ii) 0.0026

(c) (i) 0.0746 (ii) 0.0655

(d) Discrete distribution being approximated by a continuous distribution.

7 (b) 0.5

(d) $\frac{13}{18}$

(e) 4.12